Horizons

Phonics and Reading

K

Book 2
Lessons 41–80

Author: Pollyann O'Brien, M.A.

Editor: Alan L. Christopherson, M.S.

 AOP   804 N. 2nd Ave. E.   Rock Rapids, IA 51246-1759   800-622-3070   www.aop.com

Horizons Phonics K, Book 2
© MM by Alpha Omega Publications, Inc.
804 N. 2nd Ave. E.
Rock Rapids, IA 51246-1759

Printed in the United States of America

ISBN 978-0-7403-0138-4

Bible

ride

Review Silent e **Rule: When two vowels are close together in a word, the first one says its own name, and the other one is silent as in** tām∉, fīl∉, dōm∉ **and** cūb∉.

① **Look at the pictures below. Put a circle around those you hear with the** long ī **sound as in** fīl∉.

bike   brim   hide   bride

tire   kite   fire   crib

195

2 **Print the words that have a short vowel sound. Then after each word add a silent ḝ, cross it out, and make a straight line over the ī.**

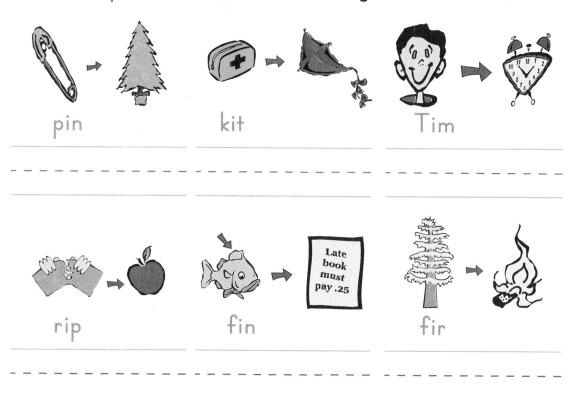

pin   kit   Tim

- -

rip   fin   fir

- -

3 **On the lines below, write the words that match the pictures. Cross out the silent ḝ and put a straight line over the vowel i to show it has the long ī sound.**

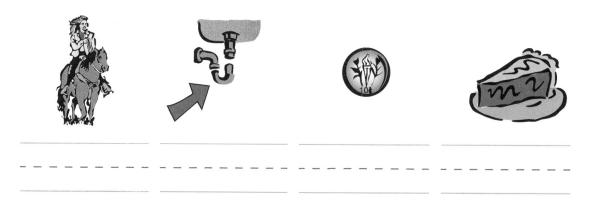

- -

4 **Draw a line from the word to the picture it matches.**

shine

kite

dime

fire

pine

5 **Read the sentences. Draw a line to match the picture.**

Jane can hide
in a shed.

Jake has a dime
in his hand.

Ike has a red
and white kite.

Mike has time
to fix his tire.

6 **Read the make-up words.**

brife   blape   chade   thide

197

7 Draw a line from the puzzle phrase to the picture it matches.

a bride on a vine

a pipe on a hike

bite a pine

wipe a dime

8 Finish spelling the words under the pictures.

f　ve　r　de　b　ke　p　e

t　me　　ne　p　pe　n　ne

drill

drum

The consonant blend dr is used at the beginning of a word.

The dr makes the sound we hear at the beginning of drive.

1 Put a circle around the pictures that start with the sound of dr.

drum   dress   drive   crane

class   draw   drip   drill

2 Practice printing Dr with a capital D.

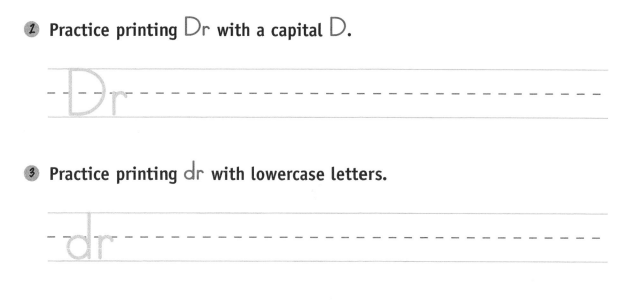

3 Practice printing dr with lowercase letters.

4 Draw a line from the word to the picture it matches.

drum

drip

thin

dress

5 Print the beginning consonant blend or digraph for each word below the picture.

ick   ip   ib

6 Circle the letters that make the beginning sound you hear.

cl cr br dr   cl cr br dr   cl cr br dr   cl cr br dr

cl cr br dr   cl cr br dr   cl cr br dr   cl cr br dr

7 Read the make-up words.

dris   drem   drof   drub   drap

8 Draw a line from the puzzle phrase to the picture it matches.

a dress with a crack

a drill with a drip

a dog can drive

a drum in a crib

201

Use a question mark ? at the end of sentences that need an answer.
Use the words who, what, where, when and why. Put a question
mark ? at the end of the sentence instead of a period.
Examples: Who is at the gate?   What is your name?

9 Read the sentences. Put a question mark ? at the end of each sentence
that asks a question.

1. Who came to the lake____   3. What time is it ____

2. Where is the dress____   4. When did Mom get here ____

10 Use a question mark ? or a period . to finish the sentence.

1. What did you do____   4. I went to get a drink ____

2. Where did Jane go____   5. When will Brad go home____

3. I have a ball ____   6. Who will brush the dog ____

11 **Spell the words under the pictures.**

_____ ill   _____ ive   _____ ip

_____ ush   _____ ack   _____ ip

12 **From the word bank, write the words that rhyme on the lines below.**

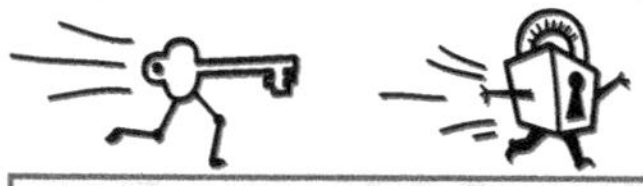

drug	drill	drip	craft	drag
draft	rag	mug	mill	chip

rug

raft

chill

brag

rip

flame

flash

The consonant blend fl is used at the beginning of a word.

The fl makes the sound we hear at the beginning of flag.

① **Put a circle around each picture that starts with the sound fl.**

flag   flash   drum   floor

float   fly   flame   dress

2 Practice printing Fl with a capital F.

3 Practice printing fl with lowercase letters.

4 Circle the letters that make the beginning sound you hear.

fl cl dr br bl

fl cl dr br bl

fl cl dr br bl

fl cl dr br bl

fl cl dr br bl

fl cl dr br bl

LESSON 43
Consonant Blend fl

5 Print the beginning consonant blend for each word below the picture.

ag   ass   ess   ack

6 Look at the pictures below. Print the word below the picture if it begins with the fl sound.

flash   flame   flip

flat   flock   flag

7 Write the words in alphabetical order.

flag   dog   cat   baby

1. _____   3. _____

2. _____   4. _____

8 Look at the pictures. Choose the correct word from the word bank to complete the sentence. Print the word on the lines below.

| flip | drake | flag | fire |

1. Tom can _____ his legs.

2. The _____ is on the lake.

3. Mike has a red, white, and blue _____.

4. Jake had a _____ in the sand.

9 Read the make-up words.

flig   flime   flane   flup   fleb

LESSON 44
Silent e: ā~~e~~ & ī~~e~~

Review Silent e **Rule:** When two vowels are close together in a word, the first one says its own name, and the other one is silent as in fī l~~e~~, dā t~~e~~, hō m~~e~~, cū t~~e~~.

1 **Look at the pictures below. Put a circle around those you hear with the** long ā **sound.**

wave   cake   rake   ant

cut   game   cane   cave

2 **Look at the pictures below. Put a circle around those you hear with the** long ī **sound.**

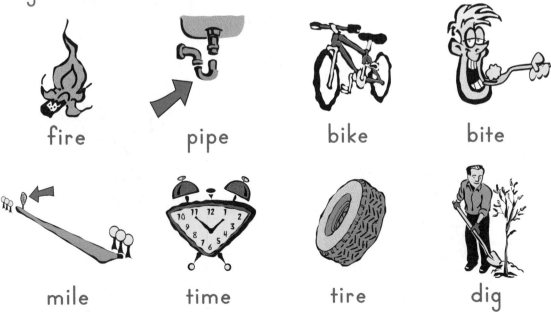

fire   pipe   bike   bite

mile   time   tire   dig

209

3 Print the words from the word bank that have a long ā or a long ī sound. Put them in the long ā column or the long ī column.

| Mike | lake | file | bake | time | wave |

Long ā **words**   Long ī **words**

---

4 Draw a line from the word to the picture it matches.

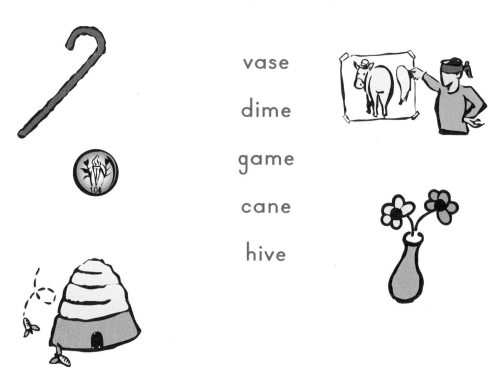

vase

dime

game

cane

hive

5 Circle the word your teacher reads. Print the words you circled on the lines below.

bake	bike	mile

vase	dike	dame

same	tame	ride

line	tape	dive

6 Spell the words below the pictures by printing the correct long vowel sound.

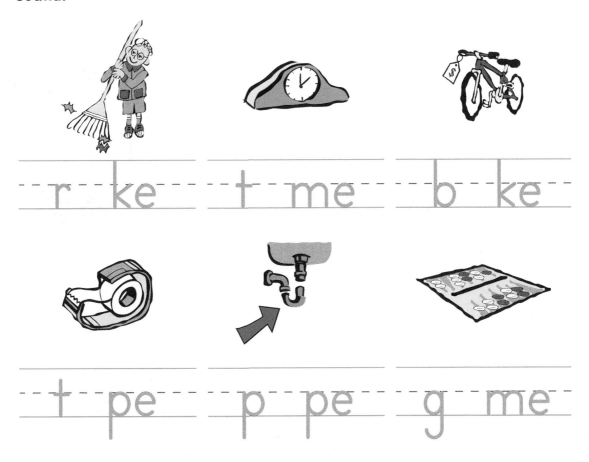

r __ ke   t __ me   b __ ke

__ t __ pe   p __ pe   g __ me

211

7 **Look at the pictures. Print the correct word from the word bank to complete the sentences.**

| game | wave | bike | pie |

1. Jake will _____ to Bill.

2. Mike has a _____ to ride.

3. The _____ is fun for Sam.

4. Take a bite of _____ .

Review **Silent e Rule:** When two vowels are close together in a word, the first one says its own name, and the other one is silent as in mālǝ, tīmǝ, cōdǝ, blūǝ.

① **Look at the pictures below. Put a circle around those you hear with the** long ā **sound.**

| drake | shave | blade | hide |

| milk | brake | wave | flame |

② **Look at the pictures below. Put a circle around those you hear with the** long ī **sound.**

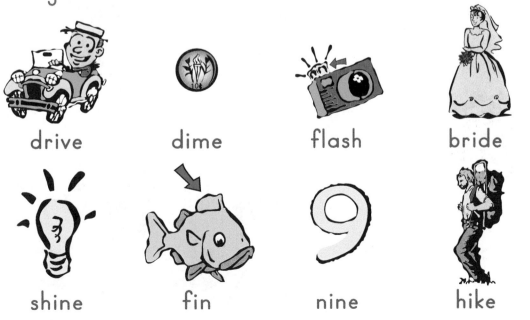

| drive | dime | flash | bride |

| shine | fin | nine | hike |

213

3 Print the words from the word bank that have a long ā or a long ī sound. Put them in the long ā column or long ī column.

| drive | brake | bride | drake | crate | white |

Long ā **words**

Long ī **words**

4 Draw a line from the word to the picture it matches.

shine

bike

hive

brake

drive

214

5 **Circle the word your teacher reads. Print the words you circled on the lines below.**

time	tire	bride

dime	brake	five

drake	fire	nine

hive	bake	lake

6 **Spell the words below the pictures by printing the correct** long vowel **sound.**

f re   d ve   h ve

D ve   s le   dr ve

215

7 **Look at the pictures. Print the correct word from the word bank to complete the sentence.**

| cake | drive | tire | bike |

1. Dad will _____ a mile.

2. Mike has a _____ for sale.

3. Dave can fix a _____ .

4. Jake has a red and white _____ .

8 **Trace, then finish the sentence by writing your name. Be sure to start your sentence with a capital letter and finish it with a period.**

My name is _____

216

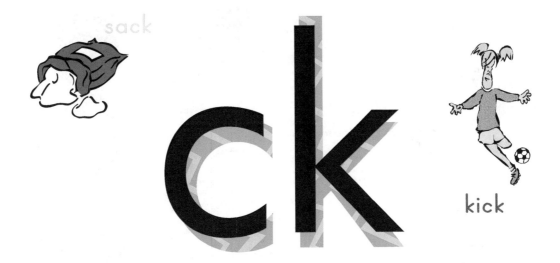

sack

ck

kick

When the consonants ck are together at the end
of a word, we hear only the one sound as in Dick.

1 Put a circle around the pictures that have the sound of ck at the end
of the word.

| kick | duck | black | fix |

| lock | math | tack | clock |

217

2 Look at the pictures below. Print the vowel in the word.

st_ck   br_ck   d_ck

d_ck   bl_ck   s_ck

3 Read the sentences. Draw a line from the picture to match the sentence. Underline the words that end with ck.

Jack has a rock
in his sock.

Dick can pick
up the shells.

The stick is
in the can.

Rick has a
big check.

4 **Print the words from the word bank on the lines next to the word that rhymes with it.**

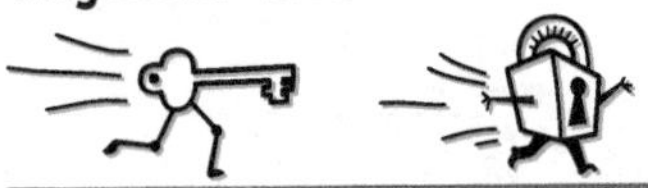

rock	buck	deck	Rick	duck
peck	tick	sack	dock	kick
pack	sock	tuck	rack	check

sick

luck

back

neck

lock

5 Print these words in alphabetical order.

tick clock back

------

buck sack duck

Jack neck rock

------

6 Draw a line from the puzzle phrase to the picture it matches.

a duck
with a wig

a fish
can kick

Jack in
a box

a pig with
a pack

7 Spell the words to match the pictures.

 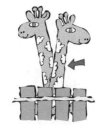 

8 Read the make-up words.

dack   jick   teck   guck   yock

9 Draw a line from the puzzle phrase to the picture it matches.

flap the cloth

a flame on a hand

a flock of cats

fan a flat

10 **Print the question sentence below. Be sure to start with a capital letter and end with a question mark.**

Where is the fire?

wing

driving

chopping

The letters ing can be used as part of a base word. The word begins with an initial consonant and ends with ing. These letters make the sound you hear at the end of the words like wing, thing and sing.

1 Look at the pictures. Put a circle around the ing sound you hear at the end of the word for the pictures below.

ring   sing   wing   ding

pink   bring   thing   fling

223

The letters ing can be used as a word ending. When ing is added to a word it means that it is happening NOW. These letters make the sound you hear at the end of words like fishing, helping or boxing.

Sometimes the last consonant in a short word is doubled before adding the ing.

Examples: sitting, running, or winning.

1. Look at the words below. The pictures show that it is happening NOW. Put a circle around the ing sound you hear at the end of the words.

| sitting | mixing | hitting | cutting |
| fixing | jogging | jumping | buzzing |

3. Put a circle around the words your teacher reads.

fixing	rock	six

locking	Jack	box

kick	kicking	take

fish	ship	mending

224

- - - - - - - - - - - - - - - - - -

④ Look at the pictures and the names below the person. Answer the questions by printing the name of the person on the lines.

Jan   Dick   Dad   Jack

Who is napping?   Who is milking?

- - - - - - - - - -   - - - - - - - - - -

Who is boxing?   Who is jogging?

- - - - - - - - - -   - - - - - - - - - -

⑤ Read the sentences below. Draw a line to the picture that it matches. Underline each word that has the ing sound.

Rick is sitting on a bench.

The cat is licking its leg.

Jake is packing his sack.

Dad is hunting for a buck.

225

6 **Look at the word pairs in the word bank. Fill in the word using ing to show it is happening NOW.**

| raft·rafting   dump·dumping   box·boxing   mix·mixing |

1. Dan is on a raft. Dan is _____.

2. Brad has trash to dump.

   Brad is _____ the trash.

3. Dave likes to box. Dave is _____.

4. Mom likes to mix a cake.

   Mom is _____ a cake.

7 **Print the words from the word bank on the lines below the word that rhymes with it.**

| pumping   telling   wishing   mopping |

yelling _____   jumping _____

hopping _____   fishing _____

‾ ‾ ‾ ‾ ‾ ‾ ‾ ‾ ‾ ‾ ‾ ‾ ‾ ‾ ‾ ‾ ‾

1 **Put a circle around each of the pictures that has a short vowel.**
   Underline the short vowel.

| game | sand | fox | duck |

| sun | mop | bat | dive |

2 **Look for the words under the pictures that have a long vowel sound.**
   Put an x on all the others.

| Bible | dine | desk | fire |

| pipe | milk | gate | pen |

227

③ **Draw a line from the word to the picture it matches.**

Jake

net

fix

bike

tub

④ **Read the make-up words.**

bame   dis   fam   sef   ket

⑤ **Draw a line from the puzzle phrase to match the picture.**

a rake
in a vase

a rock
on a cat

a leg on
a peg

a kite
on a hike

228

6 Circle the word your teacher reads. Print the words you circled on the lines below.

| fell   jell   sad | kid   kite   Kate |

| made   game   like | wade   cut   wide |

7 Look at the pictures below. Write the word from the word bank that tells about the picture.

| cake   dog   pen   game |

8 Spell the words under each picture by filling in the vowel sound you hear.

r _ ck   _ r _ t   b _ ke

_ l _ ke   _ r _ b   _ v _ n

home

cone

Silent e **Rule:** When a word has (1) a vowel, (2) a consonant, and (3) an e at the end, the first vowel sound is long and the e is silent, as in hōmę, gāmę, mīlę and tūbę.

1 **Look at the pictures below. Put a circle around those you hear with the long ō sound.**

bone   hose   rose   dome

rode   clap   rope   home

231

② Print the words that have a short vowel sound. Then after each word add a silent e, cross it out, and make a straight line over the vowel to show it has a long sound.

rod

mop

pin

rob

③ Draw a line from the word to the picture it matches.

cone

bone

hose

drove

4 **Circle the letters that make the ending sounds you hear.**

ape ope ipe

ose ise is

ate ite ote

ile ale ole

ive ove eve

ich ike oke

5 **Circle the words your teacher reads. On the lines below, print the words you have circled.**

dove	Dave	dive

rope	rose	cape

cave	kite	home

dime	nose	line

6 **Read the make-up words.**

pome   loke   jove   bobe   goke

7 **Choose the correct word to finish each sentence and print it on the line.**

Mom has a blue _____ .

cone

robe

Dave _____ into the lake.

home

dove

Blake _____ his bike home.

rode

like

The dog has a red _____ .

cape

nose

8 **Draw lines to match the words that rhyme.**

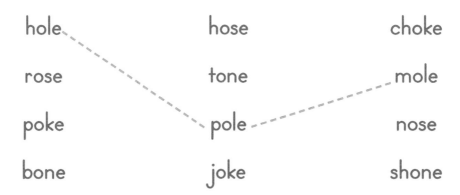

hole   hose   choke

rose   tone   mole

poke   pole   nose

bone   joke   shone

The consonant blend gr is used at the beginning of a word.

The gr makes the sound we hear at the beginning of grass.

1 Put a circle around the pictures that start with the sound of gr.

| Grace | branch | grove | grin |

| grave | grass | grill | drake |

2 Practice printing Gr with a capital G.

Gr

3 Practice printing gr with lowercase letters.

gr

4 Circle the letters that make the beginning sound you hear.

cl cr bl fl gr   cl cr bl fl gr   cl cr bl fl gr

cl cr bl fl gr   Cl Cr Bl Fl Gr   cl cr bl fl gr

5 Read the make-up words.

grame   grap   gris   gred   grut

6 Draw a line from the word to the picture it matches.

grin

grill

flag

drip

grape

7 Print the words in alphabetical order.

grass   flash   desk   crash

1. _____   3. _____

2. _____   4. _____

8 **Draw a line from the puzzle phrase to the picture it matches.**

grab a grill

a gray dog
with red legs

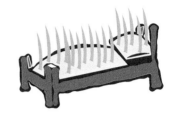

grass on
the bed

a grave
in a box

9 **Find these words in the word search.**

Circle the words that go across: grab drum greet

Circle the words that go down: grand gray flake

```
W V Q G Y F A
V C N R P L R
A Z M P L A P
I O K H J K H
V W G R E E T
N X R S V C T
G R A B A Z B
R B N M R S C
A P D R U M Q
Y W E T B C A
```

238

10 **Finish each sentence with a word from the word bank.**

| gray | grove | green | grab |

1. I like grass that is _____.

2. Did the dog _____ the bone?

3. Grace has a _____ cape.

4. We made camp in a _____.

11 **Print the beginning consonant blend for each word below the picture.**

_____ een   _____ ame   _____ ab

_____ ace   _____ ove   _____ ave

239

¹² **Write the sentence.**

Dad has a note for me.

¹³ **Color the picture.**

A= yellow   C= orange

B= green   D= blue

E= purple

glasses

Glen

glove

globe

The consonant blend gl is used at the beginning of a word.

The gl makes the sound we hear at the beginning of glass.

① Put a circle around each picture that starts with the sound gl.

| glad | Glen | glue | clam |

| glove | grin | globe | glum |

241

2 Practice printing Gl with a capital G.

3 Practice printing gl with a lowercase g.

4 Circle the letters that make the beginning sound you hear.

gl gr fr   gr fr gl   cr fr fl   gr fr fl

cr fr gl   fl cr gr   fr gr cr   fl cl gl

5 Circle the letters that make the ending sounds you hear.

ove ave ine   obe ole ode   ake oke ide   en an on

242

6 Draw a line from the word to the picture it matches.

glide

grab

glove

cross

globe

7 Circle the words your teacher reads. On the lines below, print the words you have circled.

globe	drove	clam

Glen	Mike	Grace

crime	gloss	grass

brave	blue	grave

8 Write the sentence.

I am glad to be me.

243

9 Print these words in alphabetical order.

elk apple grove drink

1. _____   3. _____

2. _____   4. _____

10 Choose the correct word to finish each sentence and print that word on the line.

1. Dan has a _____ on his desk.

globe

drove

2. Glen is _____ to be home.

grand

glad

3. Grace can _____ hop on the _____.

grass

glass

4. Dad had to _____ fix the cot with _____.

blue

glue

244

spider

sp

speedy

The consonant blend sp can be used at the beginning or at the
end of a word. When it is used at the beginning of a word,
we hear the sp sound like in the word spin.
It also makes the sound we hear at end of a word, as in wasp.

1 Put a circle around the picture that starts with the sound sp.

spell	bell	spend	spool
spade	spill	class	Spot

② Practice printing Sp with a capital letter S.

Sp

③ Practice writing sp with lowercase letters.

sp

④ Draw a line from the picture to the word it matches. Underline the beginning blend in each word.

Spot

spade

church

spill

spell

⑤ Write the sentence.

I will spend my time at school.

246

6 Read the words below. Put a circle around the pictures that end with sp. Underline the ending sp.

chicken   clasp   ship   gasp

7 Look at the pictures below. Circle the sp that shows whether the sp is at the beginning or at the end of the word.

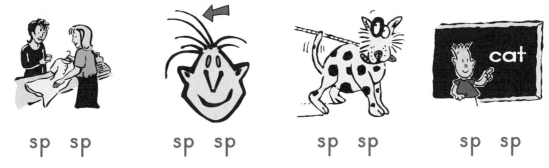

sp   sp   sp   sp   sp   sp   sp   sp

8 Read the sentences below. Draw a line from the picture to match the sentence.

Dan will clasp the
fishing rod in his hands.

Beth tells Spot
to spin.

Dad and Jake spend
time at the lake.

A black spot is
on the bench.

247

9 **Read the make-up words.**

spof   fasp   spop   posp   risp

10 **Draw a line from the puzzle phrase to the picture it matches.**

a dog spent
a dime

spin a tire

spell on a sack

spank a spot

11 **Spell the words below the picture by putting sp at the beginning or end of the word.**

ank gra   in end

248

hatch

bunch

The consonant digraphs tch and ch are used at the end of a word.
They both make the same sound we hear as in catch or ranch.

1 Put a circle around the pictures that end with ch. Underline the words
under the pictures that end with tch.

catch   ranch   inch   bunch

ditch   patch   rich   lunch

249

1 **Draw a line from the picture to the word it matches.**

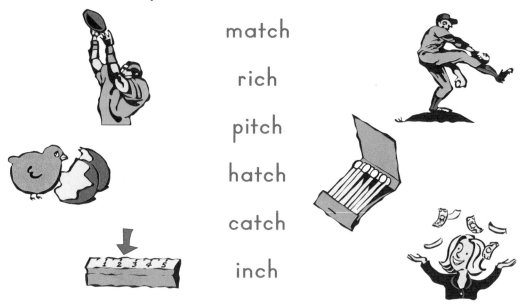

match

rich

pitch

hatch

catch

inch

3 **Read the words below. If a word ends with** ch **put a circle around the** ch**. If a word ends with** tch **underline the last three letters that make the** tch **sound.**

catch	munch	batch	Dutch	lunch
finch	ditch	latch	patch	hatch

4 **Read the make-up words.**

guch   litch   sach   metch   foch

5 **Write the sentence. Be sure to put a capital letter at the beginning and end with a period.**

I had lunch with Dad.

6 Draw a line from the puzzle phrase to the picture it matches.

a sack on
a match

catch a glass

a ranch on
an inch

pinch a fish

7 Finish spelling the words under the pictures by filling in the beginning sounds.

      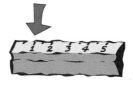

_____ ch   _____ tch   _____ ch

_____ ch   _____ ch   _____ ch

251

8 Underline the words your teacher reads. Then print the words you underlined on the lines below.

with	catch	past

lunch	hitch	glue

---

inch	gasp	crash

pinch	shave	such

---

9 Fill in the missing vowel in the crossword puzzle.

Across

2. It is your noontime meal.

3. Squeeze hard with your fingers.

Down

1. A lot of things put together.

3. Hit hard with your fist.

1. b

2. l ○ n c h

n

3. p ○ n c h
○
n
c
h

1 **Put a circle around the words that have a short ă sound, as in păn.**

cap   map   sat   dip   brag   chin

lid   bed   nap   kit   clap   flap

2 **Put a circle around the words that have a short ŏ sound, as in dŏg.**

drip   God   fun   tot   clam   rob

hop   dot   log   bun   hog   pen

3 **Put a circle around the words that have a short ĭ sound, as in fĭt.**

hid   hip   cap   bit   cot   red

jog   bib   rip   dig   lip   rim

4 **Draw a line from the word to the picture it matches.**

grape

vase

pole

game

5 Put a silent e at the end of all the short vowel words. Mark the first vowel with a straight line and cross out the silent e. Read the words and put a circle around those that have a long ā sound.

can   mad   bit

cap   Tim   fin

dim   hop   rob

6 Write the rhyming words from the word bank on the lines below.

mill	thin	fill	hot	bank	chin
dot	crank	rot	hill	win	drank

spank _____ _____ _____

spin _____ _____ _____

spot _____ _____ _____

spill _____ _____ _____

----

7 Put a silent e at the end of all the short vowel words. Mark the first vowel with a straight line and cross out the silent e. Read the words and put a circle around those that have a long ī sound.

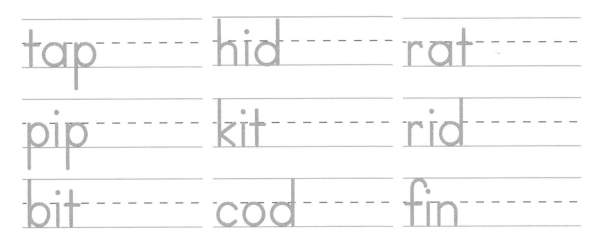

tap   hid   rat

pip   kit   rid

bit   cod   fin

8 Look at the sentences below. Underline the correct sentence to match the picture.

Five men slip in the mud.
Five men sip punch.

Jane has a game on the cot.
Sam will rest on the cot.

The dog has a big spoke.
The dog has a big bone.

I like to ride a bike.
The milk is white.

255

9 Put a silent e at the end of all the short vowel words. Mark the first vowel with a straight line and cross out the silent e. Read the words and put a circle around those that have a long ō sound.

cod   mop   pan

pip   hat   rip

not   hop   rob

10 Print the words from the word bank with the long vowel sounds in the correct column.

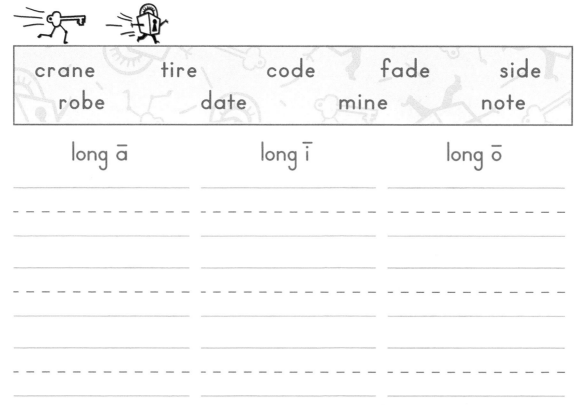

| crane | tire | code | fade | side |
| robe | date | mine | note |

long ā	long ī	long ō

11 Draw a line to match the pictures that rhyme.

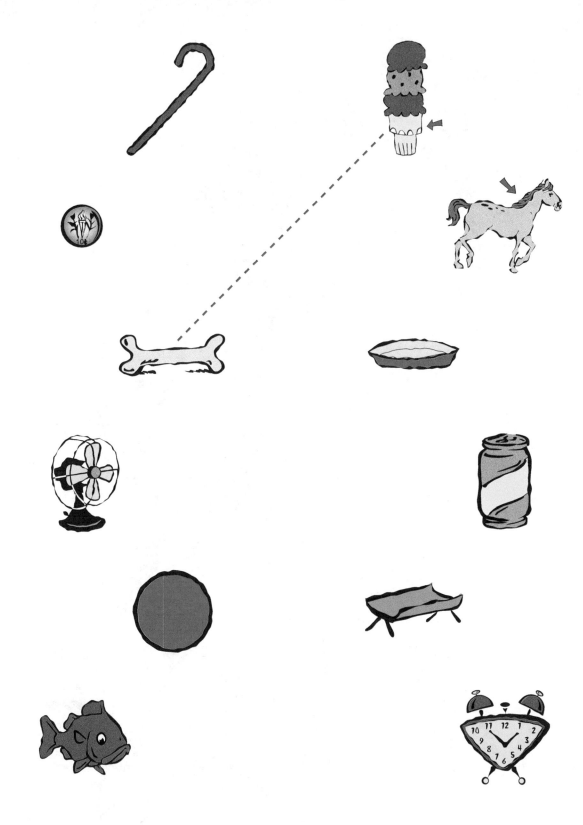

12 **Color the picture.**

June

tune

cute

Review Silent e̸ **Rule:** When two vowels are close together in a word, the first one says its own name, and the second one is silent, as in flāme̸, dīme̸, pōle̸ and cūte̸.

1 **Look, at the pictures below. Put a circle around those you hear with the** long ū **sound, as in** tūbe̸.

cube

fuse

tire

mule

clam

tube

flute

prune

2 On the lines below, write the words that match the pictures. Cross out the silent ȩ and put a straight line over the vowel u to show it has the long ū sound.

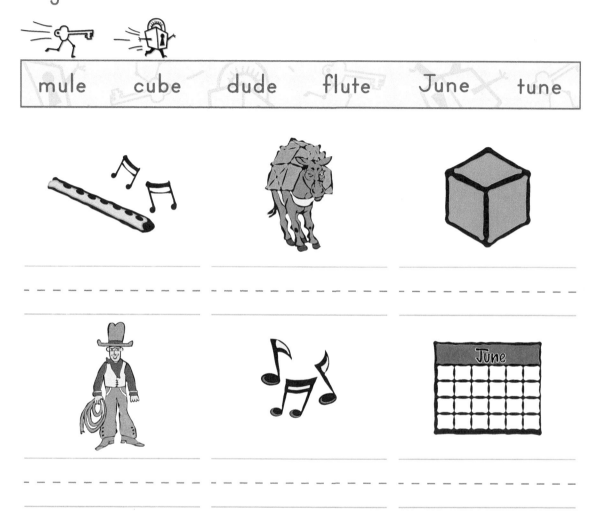

| mule | cube | dude | flute | June | tune |

3 Read the make-up words.

clume   drise   flome   grude   blaje

4 Read the sentences. Choose the correct word to fill in the blanks.

1. June is a _____ girl.

cute
cube

2. The bad boy was _____ .

tub
rude

3. Put a _____ of
   ice in the coke.

cube
cub

4. The big
   dog looks like a _____ .

brute
rule

5 Underline the word that your teacher reads.

cute	came	bun

side	mule	dike

hand	June	ride

tube	time	take

camp	hand	tune

261

6 Draw a line from the puzzle phrase to the picture it matches.

a mule
with a flute

a cube
with a fuse

Duke on
a brute

a cute pig

7 Finish spelling the words under the pictures.

m __ le   c __ be   m __ le

__ t __ ne   __ m __ le   b __ ne

262

Review the consonant blends bl, br, cl, cr, gl, gr, dr, fl, and sp.

1 Put a circle around the pictures that begin with bl. Put a square around the pictures that begin with br. On the lines below the picture, print the beginning sound to complete the spelling word.

imp   idge   ush

ick   ink   ue

ake   ead   oke

263

2 cl or cr

___ ip   ___ ib   ___ ock

___ ate   ___ ub   ___ utch

3 fl or dr

___ ag   ___ ake   ___ ess

___ um   ___ ame   ___ ip

264

4 (gl) or gr

ass   in   ove

obe   ill   ue

5 **Look at the pictures below. Circle the sp to show whether the sp is at the beginning or at the end of the word.**

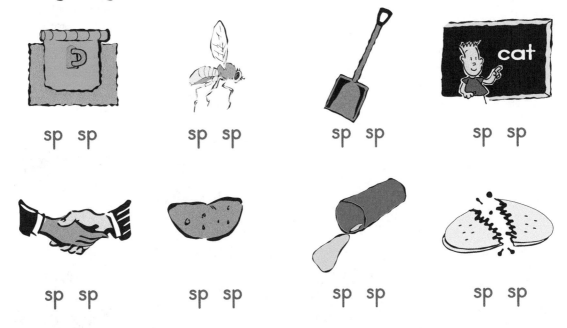

sp sp   sp sp   sp sp   sp sp

sp sp   sp sp   sp sp   sp sp

6 **Read the sentences. Choose the correct word to fill in the blanks.**

1. Nan had some _____ to fix the book.

glue
glad

2. I had fun. I can _____.

grove
grin

3. The top can _____.

spin
spell

4. Tim can _____ the dime in his hand.

flip
flat

5. The dog will _____ the sock from the box.

drag
brag

6. The tot can _____ his hands.

clap
camp

7 Draw a line between the pictures that rhyme.

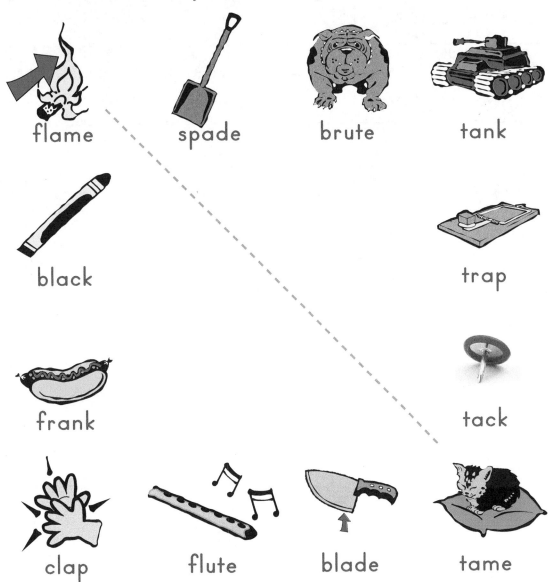

flame   spade   brute   tank

black   trap

frank   tack

clap   flute   blade   tame

8 Write the sentence. Be sure to begin the sentence with a capital letter and end with a question mark.

Can the tot go to church?

267

9 **Print the words with long vowel sounds on separate rows.**

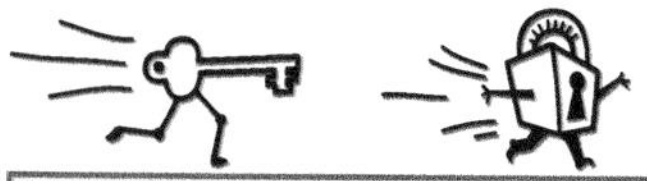

tune	like	grade	lone	mule	tape
cone	Dave	time	dive	cute	dome

Long ā

Long ō

Long ī

Long ū

268

1 Circle the letters that make the beginning sound you hear.

b d f g   b d f g   b d f g   b d f g

b d f g   b d f g   b d f g   b d f g

h j k l   h j k l   h j k l   h j k l

h j k l   h j k l   h j k l   h j k l

Review: Beginning Consonants/Blends

1 **Circle the letters that make the beginning sound you hear.**

m n p qu   m n p qu   m n p qu   m n p qu

m n p qu   m n p qu   m n p qu   m n p qu

r s t v   r s t v   r s t v   r s t v

r s t v   r s t v   r s t v   r s t v

3 Circle the letters that make the beginning sound you hear.

bl cl fl gl

bl cl fl gl

bl cl fl gl

bl cl fl gl

bl cl fl gl

bl cl fl gl

bl cl fl gl

bl cl fl gl

br cr dr gr

br cr dr gr

br cr dr gr

br cr dr gr

br cr dr gr

br cr dr gr

br cr dr gr

br cr dr gr

Review: Beginning Consonants/Blends

④ Circle the letters that make the beginning sound you hear.

th sh ch sp   th sh ch sp   th sh ch sp   th sh ch sp

th sh ch sp   th sh ch sp   th sh ch sp   th sh ch sp

⑤ Read the sentences. Choose the correct word to fill in the blanks.

1. Ted has ten _____.   cats
                                    cots

2. Dick can sip the _____.   milk
                                         mill

3. Bob has lost his _____.   log
                                         box

plant   stand

nd nt

When the consonants nd are together at the end
of a word, we blend them together, as in hand.

1. Put a circle around the pictures that have the sound of nd at the end
of the word. Print the words you have circled.

hand   fed   sand   bend

_____   _____   _____   _____

_____   _____   _____   _____

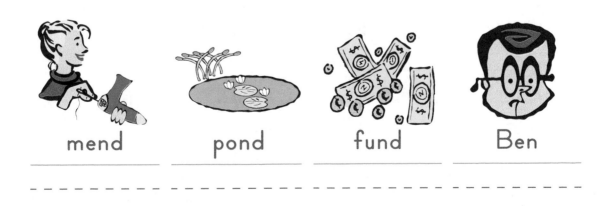

mend   pond   fund   Ben

_____   _____   _____   _____

_____   _____   _____   _____

273

When the consonants nt are together at the end of a word,
we blend them together, as in ant.

2 Put a circle around the pictures that have the sound of nt at the end
of the word. Print the words you have circled.

bent   mint   vent   hat

- -

tent   den   dent   hunt

- -

3 Circle the words your teacher reads.

ant	band	bent		tent	send	fond
sand	land	dent		mend	went	runt

274

④ **Circle the correct ending nt or nd for each of the pictures below.**

nt nd   nt nd   nt nd   nt nd

nt nd   nt nd   nt nd   nt nd

Rule: A noun names a person, place or thing.

⑤ **Read the nouns that name a person. Draw a line to the picture it matches.**

Dad

Mom

Dr. Tim

Beth

6 **Read the nouns that name a thing. Draw a line to the picture it matches.**

horse

dog

home

swing

7 **In the sentences below, underline the noun that names the person.**

Draw a line to the picture it matches.

Tom has a red
car in the sand.

Jim can bend
the wire.

8 **In the sentences below, put a circle around the noun that names a thing.**

Draw a line to the picture it matches.

The pond is big.

Bill will send his
dog to a tent.

276

hang

ng

sing

When the consonants ng are together at the end of a word, we blend them together, as in sang.

1 **Put a circle around the pictures that have the sound of ng at the end of the word. Print the words for the pictures you have circled.**

hang

rang

long

hand

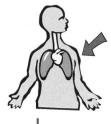

lung

band

sang

gang

277

1 **Circle the correct ending, ng, nd, or nt, for each of the pictures below.**

ng nd nt   ng nd nt   ng nd nt   ng nd nt

ng nd nt   ng nd nt   ng nd nt   ng nd nt

3 **Underline the nouns that name a person.**

Brant   dog   Bob   cat   horse   Beth

4 **Underline the nouns that name a thing.**

hand   Jim   song   tent   Jill

5 **Circle the words your teacher reads.**

| gang   sang   sand | band   ant   send |
| tent   hang   bend | lung   long   ring |

6 Look at the pictures below. Underline the correct sentence to match
   the picture. Put a circle around all the nouns that are names of people.

The gang went to see the band.
Bob went to see the land.

Don had a hand in the pond.
Jan sang a song at the pond.

Dad sang the bell at church.
Dad rang the bell at church.

The ant was in a tent.
The mint was in a tent.

7 **Find the pictures that rhyme with the following words.**

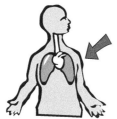

and

rung

bang

sent

8 **Write the sentence.**

I had fun when I sang a song.

9 **Read the sentences. Choose the correct word to fill in the blanks.**

bone

1. The dog had a _____.   dove

2. Mom can _____
   bake a big _____.   cane
                                  cake

3. A clock _____   time
   can tell _____.   Tim

4. It is hot in _____.   tune
                                  June

5. Jon has _____   tub
   fun in the _____.   tag

281

10 **Look at the pictures below. Choose a word from the word bank that tells about the picture.**

ant	mend	hunt	hand

1. Dad has a gun so he
   can get a buck.

2. A black and red bug
   is in the sand.

3. Mom will fix
   my socks.

4. I can print with this.

11 **Write the sentence.**

I like to grin.

tank

bunk

When the consonants nk are together at the end of
a word, we blend them together, as in bank.

① Put a circle around the pictures that have the sound of nk at the end
of the word.

bank   pink   sand   sink

wink   Hank   junk   bent

② Print five of the circled words ending with nk.

283

3 Circle the correct ending for each of the pictures below.

nk ng nd nt   nk ng nd nt   nk ng nd nt   nk ng nd nt

nk ng nd nt   nk ng nd nt   nk ng nd nt   nk ng nd nt

4 Look at the pictures. Choose the correct word from the word bank to complete the sentence. Print the words on the lines below.

| tank | bank | mint | junk |

1. Dad had some _____
   in the tent.

2. Bill will get _____
   wet in the big _____.

3. Jeff has ten _____
   dimes to put in the _____.

4. The ant is on the _____.

284

⑤ **Circle the words your teacher reads.**

bank	sang	mink	send

hand	pond	ant	kink

bang	bent	Hank	mend

junk	rang	tent	lung

⑥ **Draw a line from the words on the left to the words on the right that rhyme.**

bank

bunk

hand

sang

sent

tank

junk

tent

Hank

gang

bent

band

rang

dent

sand

bang

land

hang

7 Look at the pictures. Read the question sentences. Circle yes or no to answer the question.

Is the runt pig in the pen?   Is the red ant on Bill's hand?

yes   no   yes   no

Did Jim set up the tent yet?   Did Hank ride in a van?

yes   no   yes   no

Can Jill wink?   Did the wind put a pile of

yes   no   sand in the path? yes no

8 Choose one question sentence from above and write it on the line.
Be sure to use a capital letter for the first word and finish with a
question mark. (?)

_____

- -

LESSON 61
Review: Blends ng, nk, nd, nt

_____

- - - - - - - - - - - - - - - - -

① **Put a circle around the words that end with the sound of ng.**

Print three of the words you have circled.

gang   lung   slip   long

sang   rang   brag   fang

_____ _____ _____

- - - - - - - - - - - - - - - - - - - - - - - - - -

_____ _____ _____

② **Circle the words your teacher reads. Write the circled words on the lines below.**

gang sang land sank	sink wink hunt pond

_____ _____

- - - - - - - - - - - - - - - - - - - - - - - - - -

dent hand bend mint	think blink runt lung

_____ _____

- - - - - - - - - - - - - - - - - - - - - - - - - -

287

3 Put a circle around the words that end with the sound of nk.
Print five of the words you have circled.

bank   bent   mink   bunk

junk   wink   sink   chin

----

4 Underline the nouns that name a person. Print the names of the persons
on the lines below.

Ted   sink   tent   Jim   Hank

⑤ **Put a circle around the words that end with the sound of nd.**

Print five of the words you have circled.

hand   mend   fix   bunk

think   fund   bend   pond

⑥ **Underline the nouns that name a thing. Print the names of the animals on the lines below.**

tank   dog   band   hog   fox

289

1 **Put a circle around the words that end with the sound of nt.**

Print five of the words you have circled.

dent   tent   pond   hunt

vent   men   went   runt

------ ----------------------------

------ ----------------------------

8 Finish spelling the words under the pictures by filling in the ending sounds.

si

te

hu

ra

be

bli

me

sa

ga

9 **Print each row of words in alphabetical order.**

hang   gang   rang   bang

1. _____   3. _____

2. _____   4. _____

sink   pink   rink   mink

1. _____   3. _____

2. _____   4. _____

mend   send   lend   tend

1. _____   3. _____

2. _____   4. _____

mint   lint   tint   hint

1. _____   3. _____

2. _____   4. _____

scold   skate

SC SK

The consonant blends sc and sk are usually used at the beginning of the word. They both make the sound we hear at the beginning of skate and scab.

1 Put a circle around each picture that starts with the sound of sc. Print five of the words starting with sc you have circled.

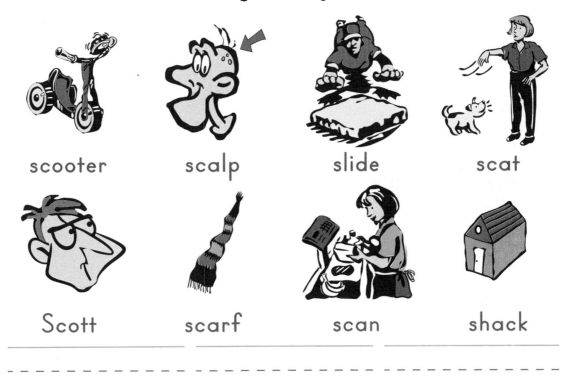

scooter   scalp   slide   scat

Scott   scarf   scan   shack

2 Put a circle around each picture that starts with the sound of sk.

Print five of the words starting with sk you have circled.

church   skirt   skillet   skip

skunk   drip   skull   skate

_ _

_ _ _ _ _ _ _ _ _ _ _ _ _ _ _ _ _ _ _ _

3 Circle the words your teacher reads.

| skip | skit | clam | | skull | song | bank |

| drink | skunk | sip | | shall | will | skill |

----

4 **Look at the pictures below. Underline the correct sentence to match the picture.**

Jack can skip on the path.
Jack can slip in the bed.

Dan can put on a skull.
Scott can run as fast as a skunk.

Don had a hole in his sock.
Bob cut the skin on his hand.

Will Meg get a red skirt?
Meg has a scab on her nose.

5 **In the sentences below, underline the noun that names the person. Draw a line to the picture it matches.**

Scott can skip in the den.

Who has Jack's cap?

Jane saw a skunk at the lake.

Did Meg scuff her shoe?

6 **Look at the pictures below. Choose a word from the word bank that tells about the picture. Print the correct word in the blanks.**

skunk	sketch	skin	skid

1. Dick can _____ his mom.

2. The _____
   ran up the path.

3. The red car will _____
   in the sand.

4. The _____ on
   Jan's hand was wet.

tusk

sk

desk

When the consonants sk are together at the end
of a word, we blend them together, as in ask.

① Put a circle around the pictures that have the sound of sk at the end
of the word. Print four of the words ending with sk you circled.

mask

desk

bunk

dusk

task

list

flask

ask

2 **Circle the correct ending for each of the pictures.**

sh th sk   sh th sk   sh th sk   sh th sk

3 **Circle the correct beginning for each of the pictures.**

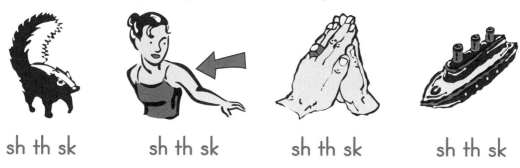

sh th sk   sh th sk   sh th sk   sh th sk

4 **Circle the words your teacher reads.**

task	that	which		chat	bank	disk
skit	ask	back		Hank	band	sink

5 Spell the words below the picture by printing the ending sounds.

nk sk ng

ma_____

nd sh nk

sku_____

ch sh ng

chur_____

nk sk sh

tu_____

ng nd nt

de_____

nk nt nd

me_____

6 Draw a line from the word to the picture it matches.

disk

mask

flask

tusk

husk

7 **Look at the pictures below. Underline the correct sentence to match the picture.**

Shad has on a mask.
Shad has on a bask.

Jill will ask Mom to go to the pond.
Jill will flask Mom to go to the pond.

Tad had a task to do in the den.
Tad had a dusk to fix in the den.

The elephant has a flask.
The elephant has a long tusk.

8 **Find the pictures that rhyme with the following words. Draw a line from the word to the picture it matches.**

risk

bask

husk

⑨ **Print each row of words in alphabetical order.**

bask   task   ask   mask

1. _____   3. _____

2. _____   4. _____

risk   husk   dusk   tusk

1. _____   3. _____

2. _____   4. _____

frisk   whisk   disk   brisk

1. _____   3. _____

2. _____   4. _____

301

10 **Follow the letters and connect the dots to make a picture.**

Color the picture.

camp

lamp

When the consonants mp are together at the end of
a word, we blend them together, as in lamp.

1 Put a circle around the pictures that have the sound of mp at the end
of the word. Print five of the words for the pictures you have circled.

camp   pup   lamp   limp

tent   jump   pump   dump

2 Circle the correct ending for each of the pictures below.

mp sk nk nd   mp sk nk nd   mp sk nk nd   mp sk nk nd

mp sk nk nd   mp sk nk nd   mp sk nk nd   mp sk nk nd

3 Print the words from the word bank that rhyme with the words below.

| ramp | limp | damp | chimp | lamp |
| lump | pump | blimp | jump |

camp _____ _____ _____

rump _____ _____ _____

wimp _____ _____ _____

Review Rule: A sentence is a complete thought that tells

who did what.

Every sentence must start with a capital letter and end with a period $(.)$ at the end of a statement, a question mark $(?)$ at the end of a question, or an exclamation mark $(!)$ to show something startling.

4 Read the exclamation sentences. Put an exclamation mark $(!)$ at the end of each sentence. Choose one sentence with an exclamation mark to print on the lines below.

When I see a dump, I jump____   Ouch, I hit my hand____

5 Read the question sentences. Put a question mark $(?)$ at the end of each sentence. Choose one question sentence to print on the lines below.

Can Meg go to camp____   Will Dad fix the lamp____

305

6 **Read the sentences. Put a period (.) at the end of each sentence.**
Choose one sentence to print on the lines below.

We can go to the pump for a drink ____

Glen and Bob will romp in the den ____

7 **Circle the words your teacher reads.**

pump	pup	punt	limp	skunk	sip
rang	camp	lung	skip	scuff	lamp

help

kelp

When the consonants lp are together at the end of a word, we blend them together, as in kelp.

1 Put a circle around each picture that ends with the sound of lp. Print three of the words that end with lp on the lines below.

tusk   gulp   scalp   help

bang   kelp   pulp   bent

2 Circle the correct ending for each of the pictures below.

lp sk mp   lp sk mp   lp sk mp   lp sk mp

lp sk mp   lp sk mp   lp sk mp   lp sk mp

3 Print all the words ending with lp on the lines below.

4 Put a circle around five things you like to do.

skip   help   run   jump   jog

skate   sing   clap   kick   bike

5 Write the sentence and fill in the blanks with the two words of your
choice.

I like to _____ and _____

the best when I have time.

6 **Print any two of the sentences below. Put a capital letter on the first word and a period at the end of the sentence.**

bill can ride his bike to camp

tom will help with the task

meg can gulp a drink

dad put his hand on his scalp

7 Print any two of the question sentences below. Put a capital letter on the first word and a question mark at the end. Be sure to put a capital letter on a person's name.

what did Ben do to help mom

did Sid wipe the dish with a rag

can Mike ring the bell

do you like white cake the best

310

8 Spell the words below by printing the correct ending sounds.

lp sh mp

he _ _ _ _ _ _

lp sh mp

la _ _ _ _ _ _

lp sh mp

cra _ _ _ _ _

nk nt nd

a _ _ _ _ _ _ _

nk nt nd

bra _ _ _ _ _

nk nt nd

pi _ _ _ _ _

9 Circle the words your teacher reads.

scalp	crab	scab

yelp	crib	slip

brand	help	crust

skunk	song	skull

⑩ **Color the picture.**

A= yellow   C= orange

B= green   D= blue

E= purple

sulk

milk

When the consonants lk are together at the end of a word,
we blend them together, as in the word milk.

1 Put a circle around the pictures that have the sound of lk at the end of
the word.

milk   silk   skip   sulk

bulk   hulk   skit   sick

2 **Read the circled words again from Activity 1 on the previous page.**
Print the vocabulary word.

1. Spell the word if you want to drink something white.

_____

2. Spell the word if you feel like a grump.

_____

3. Spell the word if you feel soft cloth on your skin.

_____

4. Spell the word if you see someone big and strong.

_____

3 **Draw a line from the word to the picture it matches.**

disk

milk

sulk

hulk

4 **Circle the words your teacher reads.**

hulk	hump	had

line	silk	mask

dusk	milk	ask

bulk	dusk	task

5 **Spell the words below the picture by printing the correct ending sounds.**

lk lp mp   lk lp mp   lk lp mp

mi   la   he

ng nd nk   ng nd nk   ng nd nk

ha   to   ba

6 **Look at the pictures below. Underline the correct sentence to match the picture.**

Jan has a silk dress.   Jack has a hat on the list.
Jan has a skip dress.   Jack is mad and will sulk.

315

1 **Read the sentences. Print them on the lines using the correct capital letters at the beginning and for a persons name. Use the correct period or question mark at the end.**

did peg drink the milk

can jan get a silk dress

tom went to the camp

will you print your name

Review endings sk, mp, lp and lk with short vowels.

1 Circle the letters that make the ending sound you hear.

ng nk nd nt   ng nk nd nt   ng nk nd nt   ng nk nd nt

2 Circle the letters that make the ending sound you hear.

lp lk mp sk   lp lk mp sk   lp lk mp sk   lp lk mp sk

3 Spell the words under each picture.

lamp   jump   dump

4. Spell the words below the picture by printing the correct ending sounds.

lp lk mp sk

ca

lp lk mp sk

gu

lp lk mp sk

tu

lp lk mp sk

sca

lp lk mp sk

mi

lp lk mp sk

ma

5. Spell the words under each picture.

hunt

band

gang

Review: Endings with Short Vowels

6 **Print the words in alphabetical order.**

clap   fund   bent   Bill

1. _____   3. _____

2. _____   4. _____

junk   vent   men   Jan

1. _____   3. _____

2. _____   4. _____

wink   band   ant   Kent

1. _____   3. _____

2. _____   4. _____

7 **Look at the words in the word bank. Print the word in the blank that makes the sentence correct.**

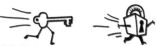

| milk | help | pink | fang | hand | sang |

1. Jan has a _____ dress.

2. Bob _____ a song.

3. Mom put a glass of _____ on the stand.

4. Put your _____ on the dog.

5. I can _____ Dad in the den.

6. The cat has a big _____ .

8 **Look at the pictures below. Underline the correct sentence to match the picture.**

Brad will drink the sink.
Brad will drink the milk.

Sam is a hulk of a man.
Sam can hand the man a cap.

320

1 **Circle the letters that make the beginning sound you hear.**

bl br cl cr   bl br cl cr   bl br cl cr   bl br cl cr

bl br cl cr   bl br cl cr   bl br cl cr   bl br cl cr

2 **Circle the letters that make the beginning sound you hear.**

dr fl gr gl   dr fl gr gl   dr fl gr gl   dr fl gr gl

dr fl gr gl   dr fl gr gl   dr fl gr gl   dr fl gr gl

³ **Look at the pictures below. Circle the sk to show if it is at the beginning or the end of the word.**

sk sk	sk sk	sk sk	sk sk

sk sk	sk sk	sk sk	sk sk

⁴ **Draw a line from the words in each column that rhyme.**

crab	slam
clip	grab
grin	blue
glue	fin
clam	slip

crib	tape
grape	bless
dress	husk
disk	rib
dusk	risk

5 **Spell the following words by filling in the beginning blends.**

imp
ue
alp

ock
ag
in

ick
ape
ove

ate
um
ake

6 **Read the sentences. Choose the correct word to fill in the blank.**

1. Dad will _____
   fix it with a _____ .   spade
                                             speck

2. Jim can _____
   his dimes for a cap.   spend
                                             spike

3. Jack put the _____
   on his hand.   glove
                                             glass

4. Jan had to _____
   the rug to fix it.   glue
                                             grab

5. I like to see you _____ .   green
                                             grin

6. Did Mom put a _____
   on the doll?   dress
                                             drive

324

7 Circle the words your teacher reads.

sink	gang	bent	band	dent	disk
wimp	hemp	brag	hand	vent	long
scalp	sent	think	sand	rang	lung
milk	long	sent	junk	pink	fang

8 Print the letters that make the ending sound you hear for each word under the picture.

fa _____   ju _____   be _____

me _____   sa _____   pi _____

9 **Put the words in alphabetical order.**

flag   scalp   glad

1. _____   2. _____

3. _____

10 **Put the words in alphabetical order.**

flake   help   glue

1. _____   2. _____

3. _____

11 **Write the sentence.**

I bless and thank God all the time.

_____

_____

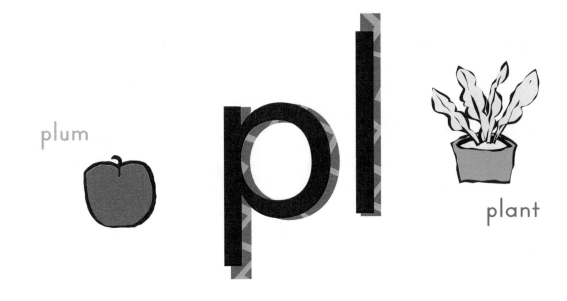

plum

pl

plant

When the consonants pl are together at the beginning
of a word, we blend them together, as in plant.

1 **Put a circle around each picture that starts with the sound pl.**

plant   planet   clamp   plank

pest   plum   play   plate

327

② **Practice printing** Pl **with a capital** P.

Pl

③ **Practice printing** pl **with a lowercase** p.

pl

④ **Circle the letters that make the beginning sound you hear.**

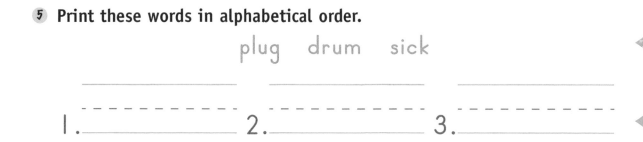

pl gl cl   pl gl cl   pl gl cl   pl gl cl

pl gl cl   pl gl cl   pl gl cl   pl gl cl

⑤ **Print these words in alphabetical order.**

plug   drum   sick

1._____ 2._____ 3._____

6 **Draw a line from the word to the picture it matches.**

plug

plus

planet

plank

drum

Review Rule:	A noun names a person, place or thing.

Review examples:

Name of a person: Bob, Mom, Jeff, Meg, Jim, Tom

Name of a thing: house, cat, horse, tent, glass

Rule:	A pronoun can take the place of a noun.

7 **Learn to read the pronouns in the word bank.**

I	he	she	you	me	they	him	her	his

8 **Write the sentence and underline the pronoun.**

I am happy.

9 Read the sentences with your teacher. Change the noun to a pronoun.

1. Brad lost the plug for his van.

   _____

   _____ lost the plug for his van.

   He
   Him

2. Meg can sit on the plank.

   _____

   _____ can sit on the plank.

   Her
   She

3. (Your name) likes to print.

   _____

   _____ like to print.

   Me
   I

4. Tom gave the plum to (your name).

   _____

   Tom gave the plum to _____ .

   me
   I

5. Jon and Sam can drive a van.

   _____

   _____ can drive a van.

   Them
   They

6. The dog can go home with Jeff.

   _____

   The dog can go home with _____ .

   his
   him

   _____

   It is _____ dog.

   his
   he

7. The cat can rest on the cot with Jan.

   _____

   The cat can rest on the cot with _____ .

   her
   she

330

LESSON 70
Review: Beginning Consonant Blends

1 Circle the letters that make the beginning sounds you hear. Print two of the words that begin with br on the lines below.

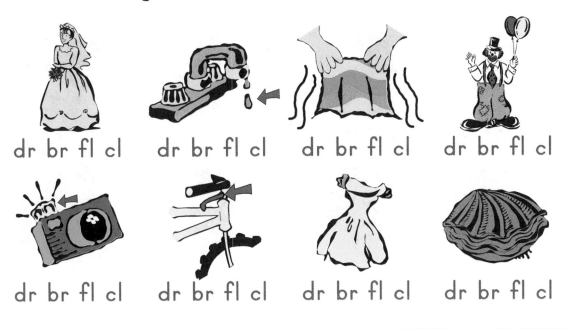

dr br fl cl   dr br fl cl   dr br fl cl   dr br fl cl

dr br fl cl   dr br fl cl   dr br fl cl   dr br fl cl

2 Underline the pronouns in the sentences below.

She has a blue dress.

He can go to the lake.

They will get to run up the path.

Will you sing a song?

I like to camp.

Buff is his dog.

331

③ Circle the letters that make the beginning sounds you hear. Print two of the words that begin with gl on the lines below.

cr gr gl fl   cr gr gl fl   cr gr gl fl   cr gr gl fl

cr gr gl fl   cr gr gl fl   cr gr gl fl   cr gr gl fl

④ Circle the letters that make the beginning sounds you hear. Print two of the words that begin with ch on the lines below.

sp pl ch sh   sp pl ch sh   sp pl ch sh   sp pl ch sh

sp pl ch sh   sp pl ch sh   sp pl ch sh   sp pl ch sh

5 **Underline the nouns in the sentences below.**

The dog and the cat sat in the tent.

Jeff and Ned can go to camp.

6 **Print the nouns which are the names of persons or things.**

dog   cat   tent   Jeff   Ned

7 **Print the pronouns in the word bank on the lines below.**

| she | he | they | you | I | his |

8 **Make up a sentence to tell your teacher. Use the pronoun** I.
Start it with I like to...

_____

- -

_____

- -

_____

9 **Draw a picture of what you like to do.**

mail

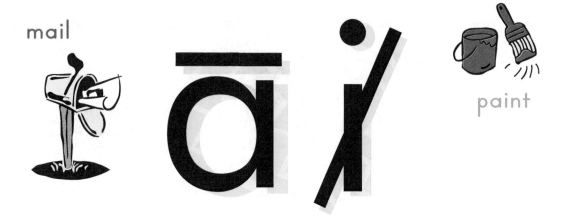

paint

Rule: When two vowels are close together, the first one is long (says its own name) and the second one is silent.

Examples: tāil, hāir, māil, chāin

1 Look at the pictures below. Put a circle around the pictures that have the long ā sound.

bat   Gail   mail   jail

pail   fan   rain   hair

2 On the lines below, print the words that match the pictures. Cross out
the second vowel and make a straight line over the first vowel to show
that it has a long sound.

pail

pain

quail

sail

faith

3 Draw a line from the word to match the picture.

paint

tail

sail

nail

bait

336

LESSON 71
Double Vowels ai

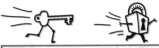

4 Print four of the words from the word bank that rhyme with the word Gail.

| tail | sail | nail | rail | mail |

5 Read the make-up words.

naid   shaib   gaid   laif   plaip   blaig

6 Draw a line from the puzzle phrase to the picture it matches.

a nail with bait

paint the quail

a tail on Gail

hair in a pail

7 **Read the sentences. Choose the correct word to complete the sentence.**

1. Gail ran to get the _____ .

main
mail
paid

2. Jane had a _____ of rain water.

pain
sail
pail

3. The hen _____ ten eggs in the nest.

paid
laid
lain

4. We _____ the maid ten dimes.

paid
pain
paint

5. Sam put the _____ on the fish line.

wait
gain
bait

8 **Write the sentence.**

I have faith in God.

_____

338

LESSON 72
Consonant Blend with ai

snail

braid

1 **Put a circle around the pictures that have the long ā sound.**

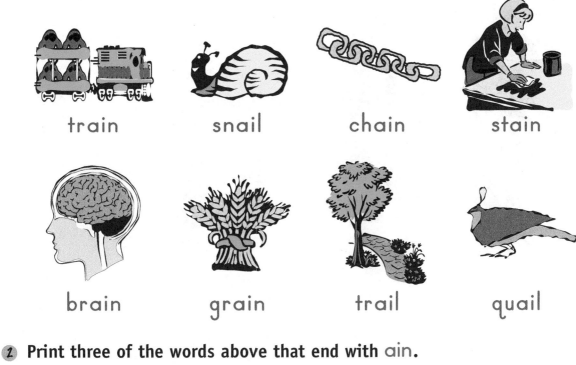

train   snail   chain   stain

brain   grain   trail   quail

2 **Print three of the words above that end with ain.**

339

③ Print two of the words from Activity 1 that begin with the consonant blend tr.

_____   _____

- - - - - - - - - - - - -   - - - - - - - - - - - - - -

_____

④ Print the word that is a bird.

_____

- - - - - - - - - - - - -

_____

⑤ Put a circle around the pictures that have the long ā sound. Put an x on those that have a short vowel sound.

⑥ Read the make-up words.

chaim   braif   glaig   staip

7 **Draw a line from the sentence to the picture it matches.**

Dad had to
paint the den.

Jack has a
pair of socks.

Ann will get
the mail.

Jill has a braid
in her hair.

8 **Put the words in alphabetical order.**

bait tail sail

1. _____ 2. _____ 3. _____

aim pain brain

1. _____ 2. _____ 3. _____

grain drain quail

1. _____ 2. _____ 3. _____

rain aid bait

1. _____ 2. _____ 3. _____

9 **Choose the correct word to complete the sentence.**

1. Gail had a _____ in her hair.

braid
bad

2. The dog put his _____ on my leg.

tail
tape

3. The fish had the _____ on his lips.

best
bait

4. The men will _____ on the lake.

sail
sell

5. The _____ will go past the box.

train
trim

6. Dad ran on the _____ to the lake.

trim
trail

342

10 **Draw a line from the puzzle phrase to the picture it matches.**

a snail on
a plate

paint on
a trail

rain in
the jail

a chain on
a brain

11 **Color the picture.**

343

12 **Spell the words under the pictures.**

sail mail hair

jail nail pain

tail pail paid

truck

pray

The consonant blend pr is used at the beginning of a word.

The pr makes the sound we hear at the beginning of print.

① **Put a circle around each picture that starts with the sound pr.**

dress

press

prince

print

tong

pray

prize

primp

345

② Practice printing Pr and pr with a capital P and a lowercase p.

Pr

pr

The consonant blend tr is used at the beginning of a word.

The tr makes the sound we hear at the beginning of trap.

③ Put a circle around each picture that starts with the sound tr.

④ Practice printing Tr and tr with a capital T and a lowercase t.

Tr

tr

5 Circle the letters that make the beginning sound you hear.

tr pr dr cr

tr pr dr cr

tr pr dr cr

tr pr dr cr

tr pr dr cr

tr pr dr cr

tr pr dr cr

tr pr dr cr

Rule: Quotation marks (" ") are used to show only the exact words when a person talks. A comma (,) is used to separate the direct words from the name of the speaker.

Examples: Tom said, "I like you."
"I can go home," said Jeff.

6 Read the story sentences with your teacher.

Dale said, "I went to a big game."

Bob asked, "Did you like the game?"

Dale answered, "It was a good game."

"Can I go with you next time?" asked Bob.

"Yes," said Dale. "I want you to go with me."

347

7 Print the following sentences and put the quotation marks that show who is talking.

Dale said, I set the trap.

- -

Jim said, Jon ran on the track.

- -

- -

Can you print this note? asked Jane.

- -

- -

8 Draw a line from the word to the picture it matches.

trap

print

prong

track

truck

348

slide

slice

The consonant blend sl is used at the beginning of a word.

The sl makes the sound we hear at the beginning of sled.

1 Put a circle around each picture that starts with the sound sl.

| slice | skip | slam | sled |

| sell | slide | slant | slept |

2 Practice printing Sl with a capital S.

Sl

3 Practice printing sl with a lowercase s.

sl

4 Draw a line from the word to the picture it matches.

slept

slim

slant

slam

sled

5 Read the make-up words.

trank   spide   blag   prave

6 Circle the letters that make the beginning sound you hear.

sl sk pl   sl sk pl   sl sk pl   sl sk pl

pr tr cr   pr tr cr   pr tr cr   pr tr cr

7 Read the sentences. Draw a line from the picture to match the sentence.

Did the
cot slant?

Ted has a
red sled.

Jack has a slot
for his mail.

Beth is a
slim gal.

8 Spell the words below the pictures by printing the beginning sounds.

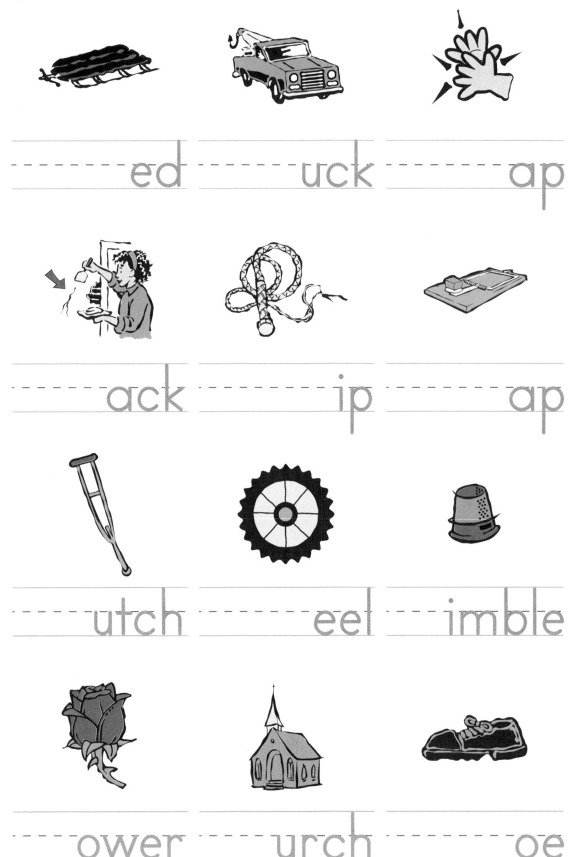

ed   uck   ap

ack   ip   ap

utch   eel   imble

ower   urch   oe

352

smell

sm

smile

smelt

The consonant blend sm is used at the beginning of a word.

The sm makes the sound we hear at the beginning of smell.

1 Put a circle around each picture that starts with the sound sm.

smelt   smash   smile   small

spell   smoke   grass   smudge

2 **Practice printing** Sm **with a capital** S.

Sm

3 **Practice printing** sm **with a lowercase** s.

sm

4 **Draw a line from the word to the picture it matches.**

smash

smell

smelt

Mr. Smith

smock

5 **Print the words in alphabetical order.**

van   nail   ant

1. _____   2. _____   3. _____

tent   wish   cat

1. _____   2. _____   3. _____

6 **Read the sentences. Draw a line from the picture to match the sentence.**

Underline the words that begin with sm.

Beth can
smell the rose.

Did Jim smash
the van?

Mr. Smith got a
smack on the lips.

A smelt is a fish.

7 **Spell the words that rhyme.**

crash	snack	fog	crack
spell	log	well	flash

smash _____ _____

smack _____ _____

smog _____ _____

smell _____ _____

8 Print the following sentences and put the quotation (" ") marks that show who is talking.

Mr. Smith said, I can have a snack for lunch.

I want a smelt for my lunch, said Tim.

9 Spell the words below the pictures.

ell   ell   oke

snowman   sn   snail

The consonant blend sn is used at the beginning of a word.

The sn makes the sound we hear at the beginning of snap.

1 Put a circle around each picture that starts with the sound sn.

snap   snack   smack   sniff

smile   snip   snug   snag

2 **Practice printing** Sn **with a capital** S.

Sn

3 **Practice printing** sn **with a lowercase** s.

sn

4 **Draw a line from the word to the picture it matches.**

snap

snack

snag

snip

_____
- - - - - - - - - - - - - - - - -
_____

5 **Read the sentences. Draw a line from the picture to the sentence it matches. Underline the words that have sn at the beginning.**

Jan is such
a snob.

Bill saw a snake
under the tent.

It is a snap to
slap and clap.

I had a smelt
for my snack.

6 **Look at the set of sentences below. Underline the correct sentence to match the picture.**

The band can snap.
The band can hand.

The tot had a snip for lunch.
The tot had a snack for lunch.

Beth's sock had a snug in it.
Beth's sock had a snag in it.

The bad man had to snatch the mask.
The bad man had to smock the mask.

7 **Spell the words that rhyme.**

| flap | wag | flip | rag | ship | crack |
| track | whack | sag | hip | trap | map |

snap _____ _____ _____

snack _____ _____ _____

snag _____ _____ _____

snip _____ _____ _____

8 **Circle the words your teacher reads.**

snap	smog	stem
fog	slip	snack

snug	bug	tug
grab	snag	bluff

---

1 **Circle the letters that make the beginning sounds you hear.**

pr dr fl gr   pr dr fl gr   pr dr fl gr   pr dr fl gr

sn pl sm gl   sn pl sm gl   sn pl sm gl   sn pl sm gl

sl tr sp cl   sl tr sp cl   sl tr sp cl   sl tr sp cl

sk cr fr bl   sk cr fr bl   sk cr fr bl   sk cr fr bl

361

② **Circle the letters that make the beginning sounds you hear.**

sc br sn gr

sc br sn gr

sc br sn gr

sc br sn gr

ch sh wh th

ch sh wh th

ch sh wh th

ch sh wh th

③ **Circle the words your teacher reads.**

think whisker ship	crane drape flap
blend brag clip	grab glass spot

_____

_____

④ **Listen to the words your teacher reads. Put a circle around the last sound of the word she or he says.**

| sp | ch | nd | nt | ng | nk | sk | mp | lp | lk |

1. lisp   scat   smell
2. sang   skip   plane
3. smug   church   snap
4. slam   snag   hand
5. skull   sent   skid
6. sink   slap   fang
7. link   class   grade
8. disk   flop   drain
9. clap   milk   dress
10. scalp   camp   prom

⑤ **Use some of the endings from the word bank above to make your own make-up words.**

pra_____   spi_____

cle_____   tro_____

6 **Draw a line from the puzzle phrases to the picture it matches.**

a dog
with wheels

a cat
on skates

a trap on
a hand

a test on
a chest

leaf

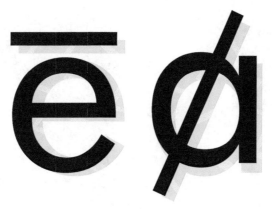

beach

Rule: When two vowels are close together, the first one is long (says its own name) and the second one is silent.
Examples: bēạt, tēạm, sāįl, lōạd

1 **Look at the pictures below. Put a circle around the pictures that have the long ē sound.**

bean

hear

leaf

dress

ear

chain

team

seat

2 Draw a line from the word to match the picture.

lead

beast

reach

sea

3 On the lines below, print the words that match the pictures. Cross out the second vowel to show that it is silent and make a straight line over the first vowel to show that it has a long sound.

ear

Jean

beard

speak

cream

heat

4 Print the words that rhyme.

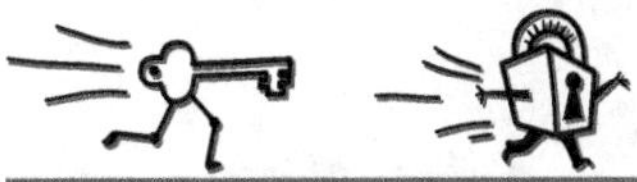

dream	deal	gear	meat	fear	heal
spear	eat	team	veal	cream	heat

ear

beam

real

seat

5 Write the sentence.

The team can eat the treat.

6 Read the make-up words.

neaf   teab   reaj   beag

7 **Read the sentences. Choose the correct word to complete the sentence.**

1. Jean can _____
   sit on the _____ .

dream
beach

2. Did you feel the _____
   from the fire?

hear
heat

3. I can eat a _____ .

peach
preach

4. Dean has a _____
   plant.

bean
beam

5. Can you _____
   a seal to read?

teach
team

6. Sam had _____ to
   eat for his meal.

Mike
meat

8 Draw a line from the puzzle phrase to the picture it matches.

a peach
can read

Jean on
a seal

reach for
the beard

teach a seat

9 Spell the words under the pictures, filling in the beginning and ending sounds.

___ea___   ___ea___   ___ea___

369

⑩ Spell the words under the pictures, filling in the double vowels in the middle.

D _ _ n   sp _ _ k   cr _ _ m

tr _ _ n   m _ _ t _ n   n _ _ l

creek   bee   meet

Review Double Vowel Rule: When two vowels are close together, the first one is long (says its own name) and the second one is silent. **Example:** sēe̸, trāi̸l, tēa̸m, chēe̸k

1 Look at the pictures below. Put a circle around the pictures that have the long ē sound.

beet   weep   pail   sweep

bed   creek   three   seed

371

② On the lines below, print the words that match the pictures.

Cross out the second vowel to show that it is silent and make a straight

line over the first vowel to show that it has a long sound.

meet

sweep

sheet

fleet

greet

③ Draw a line from the word to the picture it matches.

weep

meet

seed

wheel

queen

4 **Print the words that rhyme.**

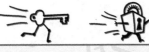

see	weed	meet	tee	deed	fee
fleet	jeep	bleed	keep	cheep	greet

weep

seed

sheet

bee

5 **Read the make-up words.**

beeg   deej   meef   teep

6 **Draw a line from the puzzle phrase to the picture it matches.**

a jeep can weep

free a weed

meet a bee

feed your feet

7 **Read the sentences. Draw a line under the sentence that matches the picture.**

Dee has a bee on her cheek.
Dee has a cheek on her seat.

Teeth can be in a beet.
Dan has teeth.

Take a peek at the seals.
Take a seed at the seals.

Mom made a meal with beef.
Mom made a meal with weep.

quick

quench

When qu is used in a word, it makes the sound
we hear at the beginning of quart.

1 **Put a circle around each picture that starts with the sound of qu.**

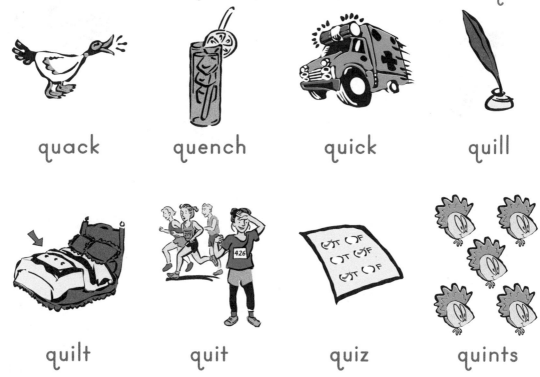

quack   quench   quick   quill

quilt   quit   quiz   quints

2 Practice printing Qu with a capital Q.

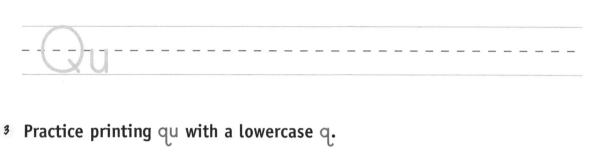

3 Practice printing qu with a lowercase q.

4 Draw a line from the word to the picture it matches.

quack

quart

quill

quilt

quick

Beginning qu & Picture Sequence

5 **Spell the words that rhyme.**

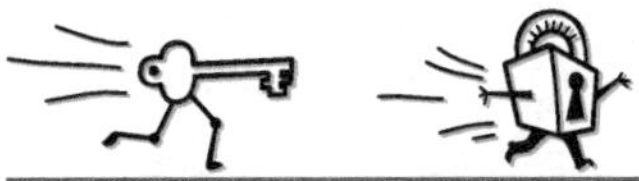

flit	Dick	back	hill	crack	flick
track	mill	slit	slick	kit	fill

quack

quit

quick

quill

6 **Read the sentences. Draw a line from the picture to match the sentence. Underline the words that begin with qu.**

The five kids
are quints.

A duck
can quack.

I can run and
I am quick.

Jan has a quilt
on her cot.

7 **Look at the two pictures. Put a circle around the one that would come first in a story.**

8 **Look at the third picture that is added to the story. Which one would come first now?**

9 Look at the two pictures. Put a circle around the one that would come first in a story.

10 Look at the third picture that is added to the story. Which one would come first now?

11 **Read the sentences. Draw a line under the one that matches the picture.**

Jean can fish with bed and wheel.
Jean can fish with a rod and reel.

12 **Spell the words under the pictures by filling in the beginning and ending sounds.**

__ ee   __ ee   __ ee

__ ee   __ ee   __ ee

382